Christmas Present, Christmas Past

from you to me®

concept by Helen Stephens
and Neil Coxon

from you to me®

Christmas Present, Christmas Past

from you to me®

This journal is for you to capture and share the magic of your Christmas.

Year after year this decoration can be updated with your precious memories and photographs telling the tale of what you did for the festive celebrations and describing your hopes for the year ahead.

This will become one of your own Christmas traditions . . . creating a story that will be treasured forever.

This Christmas journal belongs to

A bit about myself . . .

Christmas Present, Christmas Past

Year ___2014___

Christmas Eve

Where we were . . .

Who was there . . .

Some of the conversations we had . . .

What we were excited about . . .

Things that made the evening memorable . . .

We went to bed at . . .

Christmas Day

We woke up at . . .

Where we celebrated . . .

Who was there . . .

What we did . . .

Traditions we followed and/or started . . .

Christmas Day

Some of the memorable presents that were given and received . . .

What we ate and drank . . .

Christmas Day

Things that made this Christmas special . . .

Things that made us laugh and smile . . .

What was going on in the wider world?

Reflections and Aspirations

The best moments of the past year . . .

Hopes and wishes for the future . . .

Plans for the coming year . . .

Some of the 'new year' resolutions set . . .

Christmas Present, Christmas Past

Year _____

Christmas Eve

Where we were . . .

Who was there . . .

Some of the conversations we had . . .

What we were excited about . . .

Things that made the evening memorable . . .

We went to bed at . . .

Christmas Day

We woke up at . . .

Where we celebrated . . .

Who was there . . .

What we did . . .

Traditions we followed and/or started . . .

Christmas Day

Some of the memorable presents that were given and received . . .

What we ate and drank . . .

Christmas Day

Things that made this Christmas special . . .

Things that made us laugh and smile . . .

What was going on in the wider world?

Reflections and Aspirations

The best moments of the past year . . .

Hopes and wishes for the future . . .

Plans for the coming year . . .

Some of the 'new year' resolutions set . . .

Christmas Present, Christmas Past

Year _____

Christmas Eve

Where we were . . .

Who was there . . .

Some of the conversations we had . . .

What we were excited about . . .

Things that made the evening memorable . . .

We went to bed at . . .

Christmas Day

We woke up at . . .

Where we celebrated . . .

Who was there . . .

What we did . . .

Traditions we followed and/or started . . .

Christmas Day

Some of the memorable presents that were given and received . . .

What we ate and drank . . .

Christmas Day

Things that made this Christmas special . . .

Things that made us laugh and smile . . .

What was going on in the wider world?

Reflections and Aspirations

The best moments of the past year . . .

Hopes and wishes for the future . . .

Plans for the coming year . . .

Some of the 'new year' resolutions set . . .

Christmas Present, Christmas Past

Year _____

Christmas Eve

Where we were . . .

Who was there . . .

Some of the conversations we had . . .

What we were excited about . . .

Things that made the evening memorable . . .

We went to bed at . . .

Christmas Day

We woke up at . . .

Where we celebrated . . .

Who was there . . .

What we did . . .

Traditions we followed and/or started . . .

Christmas Day

Some of the memorable presents that were given and received . . .

What we ate and drank . . .

Christmas Day

Things that made this Christmas special . . .

Things that made us laugh and smile . . .

What was going on in the wider world?

Reflections and Aspirations

The best moments of the past year . . .

Hopes and wishes for the future . . .

Plans for the coming year . . .

Some of the 'new year' resolutions set . . .

Christmas Present, Christmas Past

Year _____

Christmas Eve

Where we were . . .

Who was there . . .

Some of the conversations we had . . .

What we were excited about . . .

Things that made the evening memorable . . .

We went to bed at . . .

Christmas Day

We woke up at . . .

Where we celebrated . . .

Who was there . . .

What we did . . .

Traditions we followed and/or started . . .

Christmas Day

Some of the memorable presents that were
given and received . . .

What we ate and drank . . .

Christmas Day

Things that made this Christmas special . . .

Things that made us laugh and smile . . .

What was going on in the wider world?

Reflections and Aspirations

The best moments of the past year . . .

Hopes and wishes for the future . . .

Plans for the coming year . . .

Some of the 'new year' resolutions set . . .

Christmas Present, Christmas Past

Year _____

Christmas Eve

Where we were . . .

Who was there . . .

Some of the conversations we had . . .

What we were excited about . . .

Things that made the evening memorable . . .

We went to bed at . . .

Christmas Day

We woke up at . . .

Where we celebrated . . .

Who was there . . .

What we did . . .

Traditions we followed and/or started . . .

Christmas Day

Some of the memorable presents that were given and received . . .

What we ate and drank . . .

Christmas Day

Things that made this Christmas special . . .

Things that made us laugh and smile . . .

What was going on in the wider world?

Reflections and Aspirations

The best moments of the past year . . .

Hopes and wishes for the future . . .

Plans for the coming year . . .

Some of the 'new year' resolutions set . . .

Christmas Present,
Christmas Past

Year _____

Christmas Eve

Where we were . . .

Who was there . . .

Some of the conversations we had . . .

What we were excited about . . .

Things that made the evening memorable . . .

We went to bed at . . .

Christmas Day

We woke up at . . .

Where we celebrated . . .

Who was there . . .

What we did . . .

Traditions we followed and/or started . . .

Christmas Day

Some of the memorable presents that were given and received . . .

What we ate and drank . . .

Christmas Day

Things that made this Christmas special . . .

Things that made us laugh and smile . . .

What was going on in the wider world?

Reflections and Aspirations

The best moments of the past year . . .

Hopes and wishes for the future . . .

Plans for the coming year . . .

Some of the 'new year' resolutions set . . .

Christmas Present, Christmas Past

Year _____

Christmas Eve

Where we were . . .

Who was there . . .

Some of the conversations we had . . .

What we were excited about . . .

Things that made the evening memorable . . .

We went to bed at . . .

Christmas Day

We woke up at . . .

Where we celebrated . . .

Who was there . . .

What we did . . .

Traditions we followed and/or started . . .

Christmas Day

Some of the memorable presents that were given and received . . .

What we ate and drank . . .

Christmas Day

Things that made this Christmas special . . .

Things that made us laugh and smile . . .

What was going on in the wider world?

Reflections and Aspirations

The best moments of the past year . . .

Hopes and wishes for the future . . .

Plans for the coming year . . .

Some of the 'new year' resolutions set . . .

Christmas Present, Christmas Past

Year _____

Christmas Eve

Where we were . . .

Who was there . . .

Some of the conversations we had . . .

What we were excited about . . .

Things that made the evening memorable . . .

We went to bed at . . .

Christmas Day

We woke up at . . .

Where we celebrated . . .

Who was there . . .

What we did . . .

Traditions we followed and/or started . . .

Christmas Day

Some of the memorable presents that were given and received . . .

What we ate and drank . . .

Christmas Day

Things that made this Christmas special . . .

Things that made us laugh and smile . . .

What was going on in the wider world?

Reflections and Aspirations

The best moments of the past year . . .

Hopes and wishes for the future . . .

Plans for the coming year . . .

Some of the 'new year' resolutions set . . .

Christmas Present, Christmas Past

Year _____

Christmas Eve

Where we were . . .

Who was there . . .

Some of the conversations we had . . .

What we were excited about . . .

Things that made the evening memorable . . .

We went to bed at . . .

Christmas Day

We woke up at . . .

Where we celebrated . . .

Who was there . . .

What we did . . .

Traditions we followed and/or started . . .

Christmas Day

Some of the memorable presents that were given and received . . .

What we ate and drank . . .

Christmas Day

Things that made this Christmas special . . .

Things that made us laugh and smile . . .

What was going on in the wider world?

Reflections and Aspirations

The best moments of the past year . . .

Hopes and wishes for the future . . .

Plans for the coming year . . .

Some of the 'new year' resolutions set . . .

Christmas Present,

Christmas Past

from you to me®

First published in the UK by *from you to me*, June 2009
Copyright, *from you to me* limited 2009
Hackless House, Murhill, Bath, BA2 7FH
www.fromyoutome.com
E-mail: hello@fromyoutome.com

ISBN see back cover of journal

Cover design by so design consultants, Wick, Bristol, UK
Printed and bound in the UK by CPI William Clowes, Beccles

This paper is manufactured from material sourced from forests certified according to strict environmental, social and economical standards.

Please share some of your own Christmas magic with us at the *from you to me* website to let other people read about your tales and traditions . . .

If you liked the concept of this book, please tell your family and friends and look out for others in the *from you to me* range:

Dear Mum, from you to me

Dear Dad, from you to me

Dear Grandma, from you to me

Dear Grandad, from you to me

Dear Sister, from you to me

Dear Brother, from you to me

Dear Son, from you to me

Dear Daughter, from you to me

Dear Friend, from you to me

Cooking up Memories, from you to me

These were the days, from you to me

other relationship and memory journals available soon . . .